Murder at Muckle Manor

John Townsend

Stanley Thornes (Publishers) Ltd

Originally published in 1987 by Hutchinson Education
Reprinted 1988

Reprinted in 1989 by
Stanley Thornes (Publishers) Ltd
Old Station Drive
Leckhampton
CHELTENHAM GL53 0DN

British Library Cataloguing in Publication Data

Townsend, John, *1924*—
    Murder at Muckleby Manor.—(Spirals)
    1. Readers
    I. Title   II. Series
    428.6′2   PE1119

ISBN 0 7487 0188 5

Set in Linotron Rockwell
Printed and bound in Great Britain
by Martin's of Berwick

Contents

Murder at Muckleby Manor
A Whodunnit for Twelve Parts

CAST: in order

Av	**Sir Eric Tweedhope**	M P for Muckleby-Under-Mudflap
Me	**Dame Gloria**	an actress
ames	**Rev. Dithers**	a bishop
Mark	**Lord Muckleby**	the old lord of the manor
oBert	**Lady Muckleby**	his wife
Jayne	**Giles Gray**	a young man about town
Mart A	**Bubbles**	his girlfriend
Matt	**Diggins**	the butler
	Maud	the maid
	Mrs Cloggit	the cook
	Inspector Crawls	from the Yard
	P C Dobbs	his friend

The play takes place in the drawing room of Muckleby Manor on New Year's Eve.

A complete list of Spirals

Stories

Jim Alderson
Crash in the Jungle
The Witch Princess

Jan Carew
Death Comes to the Circus

Susan Duberley
The Ring

**Keith Fletcher and
Susan Duberley**
Nightmare Lake

Paul Groves
Not that I'm Work-shy
The Third Climber

Anita Jackson
The Actor
The Austin Seven
Bennet Manor
Dreams
The Ear
A Game of Life or Death
No Rent to Pay

Paul Jennings
Eye of Evil
Maggot

Margaret Loxton
The Dark Shadow

Patrick Nobes
Ghost Writer

Kevin Philbin
Summer of the Werewolf

John Townsend
Beware the Morris Minor
Fame and Fortune
SOS

David Walke
Dollars in the Dust

Plays

Jan Carew
Computer Killer
No Entry
Time Loop

John Godfrey
When I Count to Three

Nigel Gray
An Earwig in the Ear

Paul Groves
Tell Me Where it Hurts

Barbara Mitchelhill
The Ramsbottoms at Home

Madeline Sotheby
Hard Times at Batwing Hall

John Townsend
Cheer and Groan
The End of the Line
Hanging by a Fred
Making and Splash
Murder at Muckleby Manor
Over and Out
Taking the Plunge

David Walke
The Bungle Gang Strikes Again
The Good, the Bad and the Bungle
Package Holiday

Murder at Muckleby Manor

The New Year's Eve Party is in full swing. The clock is chiming half-past eleven and the phone is ringing in the corner of the room. Sir Eric, Dame Gloria, Giles, Bubbles, the Rev. Dithers, and Lord and Lady Muckleby are busy singing and dancing the Hokey-Cokey. Diggins and Maud mingle with their silver trays of drinks and mints.

Sir Eric	You put your right foot in . . .
Gloria	Your right foot out . . .
Rev.	In . . .
Bubbles	Out . . .
Lord M.	In . . .
Lady M.	Out . . .
Giles	You shake it all about . . .
Eric	You do the Hokey-Cokey and you turn around . . .
Lady M.	That's what it's all about.
All	Ol!

Diggins	[*At the phone*] Excuse me, my lady. (He walks over to her)
All	Oh, Hokey – Cokey – Cokey!
Diggins	A telephone call, my lady.
All	Oh, Hokey – Cokey – Cokey!
Diggins	Says it's urgent, my lady.
All	Oh, Hokey – Cokey – Cokey!
Diggins	Scotland Yard, my lady.
All	Knees bend, arms bend, shout, shout, SHOUT!
Lady M.	What? Just a minute, everyone. Yes, what is it, Diggins?
Diggins	A phone call for his lordship, my lady.
Gloria	What – at this time of night?
Bubbles	On New Year's Eve?
Giles	Golly. Oh I say.
Rev.	Well, you'd better answer it while we play another game. How about 'Murder In The Dark'? That's always good for a bit of chilling fun.
Lord M.	What was that?
Lady M.	The phone, dear.
Lord M.	The what?

Lady M.	The phone, dear. It's all right – I'll answer it. He can't hear a thing after three gin and tonics. I won't be long. [*At phone*] Yes? Yes. Who? Really? Mmm Surely not. . . .
Lord M.	Where's she off to? Surely it's not bedtime yet.
Bubbles	No, uncle, she's gone to the phone. Now, how about another game? Diggins, bring in some more port, will you?
Diggins	Very well, miss.
Giles	Just be careful, Bubbles, you're getting tipsy.
Bubbles	Only a bit. I just want to wash down that super supper.
Rev.	Yes, Mrs Cloggit did us proud tonight. She's a fine cook, Lord M.
Lord M.	What was that?
Rev.	Cook – jolly fine.
Lord M.	Is it? It was snowing earlier.
Gloria	Come on, how about another party game. We've got nearly half an hour till midnight.
Eric	What a drag. I've never known such a stuffy party. I knew I should have stayed at home. I'm a very busy man, you know.
Giles	Oh don't be boring, Sir Eric. How about 'Killer Wink'?

Eric	Killer Wink? What's that, for heaven's sake?
Bubbles	Oh yes, that's super. You all have to sit round in a circle in the firelight and one of us is the murderer.
Gloria	It sounds rather dangerous.
Giles	No – the killer has to wink at the victim without being seen by anyone else. If you're winked at you die – well, pretend to! You sort of slump on the floor with a grunt.
Eric	That's nothing new, Lord Muckleby has been doing it all evening.
Lord M.	Eh?
Bubbles	And we all have to work out who the killer is without getting killed ourselves.
Eric	Sounds a daft idea to me. Anyway, how do you decide who the killer is in the first place?
Bubbles	Simple – we all take a piece of paper out of a hat – but only one piece is marked.
Giles	With an 'M'. 'M' for MURDER.
Eric	More like 'M' for MADNESS.
Gloria	Come along, Lord Muckleby, time for another game. There's going to be a murder. . . .

Lord M.	What was that?
Gloria	There's going to be a murder.
Lord M.	Then you'd better phone the police.
Lady M.	[*At phone*] I see. Goodbye. [*She turns to the guests*]. There's going to be a murder.
Lord M.	What's she on about?
Bubbles	What's wrong, auntie. You look rather pale.
Lady M.	That was Scotland Yard.
Lord M.	What was that?
Lady M.	The Yard, dear.
Lord M.	Really? Jolly chilly out there isn't it? What did you go out there for?
Lady M.	No – Scotland, dear.
Lord M.	Even colder there, I should think. You were very quick about it.
Lady M.	They phoned to say they're sending two of their men round.
Gloria	Policemen? Oh no, they'll spoil our party.
Eric	I've never heard of such nonsense in all my life. I'm sure Scotland Yard has enough to do without coming here.
Giles	But look here, how can there be a murder – there's no body!

Eric	And who would want to kill anyone here? I ask you, who on earth would want to kill me?
Bubbles	[*Under her breath*] I can think of many.
Gloria	You'd be surprised, Sir Eric.
Diggins	Port, my lady?
Maud	After-dinner mints and nuts, my lord?
Lady M.	Your nuts, dear.
Lord M.	Nonsense – I'm not balmy yet, you know.
Eric	That's what he thinks.
Lord M.	What was that?
Eric	I said, 'that's what you think.'
Lord M.	A drink? Yes, I don't mind if I do.
Bubbles	Ooh yes, I'll drink to that. Another port, please, Diggins.
Diggins	Very well, miss.
Giles	I say, steady on Bubbles, – you're tiddly.
Eric	That's nothing new. She's always sloshed. Let's face it, she needs to be to go out with you, Giles. No girl in her right mind would ever look at you.

Giles	I say! If you weren't an older man, I'd bop you on the nose. I'd take you outside for fisticuffs.
Eric	Huh! You're so short-sighted, you'd thump the wall. Let's face it, you've got to be blind to like Bubbles.
Gloria	Now look here, Eric, I think you've gone too far. This is a party and you've been nothing but a bore all evening. I can't think why you were asked here in the first place.
Eric	I might be a bore, Gloria, but at least I'm not a bankrupt old scarecrow.
Diggins	More port, my lady?
Gloria	How dare you . . . you, you, you SWINE!
Diggins	I'm sorry, I thought you might like some.
Maud	More nuts, my lord?
Gloria	I've never been so insulted in all my life.
Eric	You must have had a long life, too, if all your wrinkles are anything to go by. Anyway, I would think you are used to insults by now. Every play you've ever been in has been a flop. I've never seen such a dreadful actress.
Gloria	You'll regret saying that. You mark my words. [*She storms out*]

Giles	I say, you rotter. Now look what you've done.
Bubbles	You nasty man, Eric.
Rev.	Most uncalled for, Eric, old boy.
Lady M.	You must say sorry to her at once, Eric.
Eric	I wouldn't dream of it.
Lord M.	What's that? What's going on?
Lady M.	It's Eric, dear. He's being rude again.
Lord M.	Oh really? I say, Maud, have you got something to crack these nuts?
Maud	Your crackers, my lord.
Lord M.	What was that, my girl?
Maud	Your crackers, my lord.
Lord M.	No need to be cheeky. Anyone for a nut?
Rev.	I don't know how anyone could eat another thing after such a splendid meal. In fact I would like you to fetch Mrs Cloggit, the cook, so we can give our thanks. Off you go and fetch her, Maud.
Maud	Very well, sir. [*She goes*]
Diggins	More port, Sir Eric? A very fine one, I think you'll agree. Just right for washing down the mints.

Eric	Just leave me the bottle, Diggins. Then you can clear off. After all, we don't want a drip like you around us all night, do we?
Diggins	Very well, sir. [*He goes*]
Bubbles	I think you're being very mean tonight, Eric.
Eric	Think? Think? You can't think at all with your brain. I really don't know why I bothered to come here at all tonight with all these idiots and you, Bubbles – a drunk dumb blonde who's got less charm than a wart hog.
Rev.	Eric, you must stop all these insults. You are drinking too much. Now, let's get the party back in full swing before the clock strikes.
Lady M.	And before the police arrive.
Giles	Yes, auntie, what did they say exactly?
Eric	Must be a hoax. Someone's idea of a sick joke.
Lord M.	What was that?
Lady M.	A joke, dear.
Lord M.	Go on then, tell it to me. I like a good joke. . . .
Lady M.	Not now, dear.
Lord M.	Like the one about the three chaps in a boat.

Giles	Look, it's five to twelve.
Lord M.	Who get washed up on a desert island. . . .
Bubbles	I hope Gloria is all right. I'll go and fetch her [*She goes*]
Lord M.	. . . and the first one finds a rusty old tea pot on the sand. . . .
Lady M.	Not that old joke again, dear. You've told it three times tonight already.
Lord M.	. . . so he cleans it up a bit and FLASH! Out pops a genie. . . .
Rev.	Hurry up, everyone, it's nearly time. It's nearly the New Year.
Lord M.	'Oh Master,' he says, 'you have just three wishes. . . .'
Eric	I just wish I could get home. I'm a very busy man, you know.
Lord M.	So the chap says he'll share out the wishes with his friends – one each. 'You can have anything you like,' he says to his friend. . . .
Rev.	Is there any more port?
Giles	I think I could do with something stronger.
Eric	Too late – I've just drunk the lot.
Lady M.	I think we've all had enough drink for one evening.

Lord M.	So his friend says, 'I'd like to be off this island and at home, with a whisky in my hand.' And WOOSH, he'd gone....

[*Diggins enters with Mrs Cloggit*]

Diggins	Ladies and gentlemen, here is Mrs Cloggit, the cook.
Mrs Cloggit	How do.
Rev.	Ah, Mrs Cloggit, what a splendid meal that was. We'd all like to thank you for such a super supper.
Mrs C.	Ooh, tar very much.
Giles	Oh I say, Mrs Cloggit, it was jolly spiffing. We were all just saying what a first class nosh it was.
Eric	Were we? I'd have got more fun out of licking the back of a stamp.
Lord M.	So this chappy says to another chap. 'You can wish for anything you like.' So the second chap says to the first chap ... or was it the other way round.....
Lady M.	Come along everybody, let's join arms, it's nearly time. Yes, Diggins and Mrs Cloggit, you two must join in as well.

Mrs C.	Ee, by gum.
Diggins	Very well, my lady.
Lord M.	Anyway, the chap says, 'I wish I was at home with a drink in my hand,' and WOOSH, he'd gone as well. . . .
Eric	What is he rattling on about?
Rev.	Something to do with some chaps, I think. . . .
Lord M.	So this leaves the first chap alone on the desert island with only one wish left so he looks around him and sighs, 'I'm so lonely, I wish the other two chaps were still with me,' and WOOSH . . . Ha ha ha, good, isn't it?

[*Bubbles enters with Gloria*]

Bubbles	Come along, Gloria, the clock is about to strike.
Gloria	All right, I'll join in so long as I don't have to stand anywhere near that vile man, Sir Eric.
Eric	I couldn't care less, you old baggage.
Lady M.	Eric, don't start all that over again, we're supposed to be having fun. Come on everyone, get in the middle of the room for making a New Year's wish.

Gloria	I know what mine would be – to have a dagger in my hand right now.
Lord M.	Jolly funny joke, what? Ha ha – do you get it? WOOSH, and back they both came, ha ha. You see, the first chap brought back the other chaps ... or was it the second chap? I get a bit mixed up with my chaps.
Lady M.	Hush, dear.
Lord M.	Eh? What was that?
Lady M.	I said 'Hush,' dear. Everybody be quiet.
Diggins	I'll bring in some more drinks for the toast, my lady.
Bubbles	Golly, it's nearly time.
Giles	Oh I say, how wizzo and a spiffing good wheeze, what?
Rev.	The old grandfather clock is about to strike.
Lord M.	Grandfather about to strike? Don't be daft, he's been dead for years.
Bubbles	No, the clock, uncle. It's nearly midnight.
Rev.	Time for joining hands for a sing-song.
Giles	Oh rather – how ripping.
Bubbles	Happy New Year, Giles! [She kisses him]

Giles	Now hold your horses, it't not time yet. I say, where's the glasses to toast the New Year?
Maud	Just coming, sir. Shall I pass them round now, madam?
Lady M.	Oh yes, do. Come along everybody.
Lord M.	What was that?
Lady M.	Time for the toast, dear.
Lord M.	Don't talk daft. It's not breakfast time yet. We've only just had supper.
Eric	No, no you silly old fool – the toast we drink to bring in the New Year. And a cracking good year it's going to be too.
Giles	But how can you be so sure, Sir Eric?
Eric	Well, my lad, I've got a packet of money coming to me, that's why. I'm going to get rich, marry the woman of my dreams and get rid of all my enemies in one foul swoop.
Lord M.	Fowl soup? But we've already eaten.
Rev.	Lucky old you, Sir Eric, but I still don't know how you can be so sure.
Bubbles	Hush everyone, look at the clock....
Gloria	The midnight hour is about to strike....
Giles	I say, come on everyone, link arms....

Lady M.	Happy New Year, dear. How about a quick kiss under the mistletoe?
Lord M.	What? I say, I knew a chap once and he was so ugly that every New Year the girls used to hang him up in the corner and kiss the mistletoe!
Diggins	Will there be anything else you want, my lady?
Lady M.	Yes, Diggins, bring in the balloons and the piece of coal. It's the custom for seeing in the New Year.
Lord M.	What was that?
Lady M.	Coal, dear.
Lord M.	What?
Lady M.	Coal, dear.
Lord M.	Are you? I was just thinking it was rather warm.
Lady M.	Oh quick, everyone – join arms for 'Auld Lang Syne'.

[*The grandfather clock begins the Westminster chime. . . .*]

[*DING-DONG, DING-DONG, DING-DONG, DING-DONG*]

Giles	I say, here we go folks!

[*DING-DONG, DING-DONG, DING-DONG, DING-DONG*]

Bubbles   What fun!

[*DING-DONG, DING-DONG, DING-DONG, DING-DONG*]

Diggins   The coal, madam. And the balloons. . . .

[*DING-DONG, DING-DONG, DING-DONG, DING-DONG*]

Gloria   The end of another year!

[*DONG!*]

Rev.   And we're about to start another. Who
            knows what it will bring?

[*DONG!*]

Lord M.   What's all the fuss about?

[*DONG!*]

Lady M.   The clock, dear. This is it, midnight!

[*DONG!*]

Mrs C.   Ee by heck, it's right lovely. Give us a kiss,
            Diggins!

[*DONG!*]

Eric   I'll be glad when it's all over.

[*DONG!*]   [*Maud enters with two policemen*]

Maud   Excuse me, Madam, there's someone here
                to see you – an Inspector Crawls.

[*DONG!*]

Crawls   Scotland Yard, your ladyship ... on the
                stroke of midnight.

[*DONG!*]

P C Dobbs   The ideal time for ... a murder.

[*DONG!*]

Giles   Oh I say, how very wizard!

[*DONG!*]

Bubbles   Oh come on everyone, let's dance!

[*DONG!*]

Mrs C.   Eee yes, Knees Up Mother Brown.

[DONG!]

All   Happy New Year everybody ... yippee!

[DONG! They all sing 'Let old acquaintance be forgot ...']

Eric   Ergh umph ug yuck eek grumph... *[He slumps to the floor]*

Maud   Aaaaah! *[She faints]*

Lady M.   It's Sir Eric!

Gloria   He seems to be foaming at the mouth.

Giles   I say, mind the carpet!

Bubbles   And sort of twitching and things ...

Rev.   His lips are blue and curling at the edges ...

Mrs C.   He's wriggling and shaking all over the place.

Lord M.   Is it some sort of break-dancing?

Crawls.   Not quite, sir.

Diggins   Then what is it called?

PC   Simple ... DEATH!

Giles   You mean Sir Eric is pegging out?

Crawls   Any second now and he'll be gone for good.

Eric   Yug zz og errrrrrr!

Crawls	Told you so.
Lady M.	It must be some sort of heart attack.
PC	Nothing so pleasant as that, madam.
Maud	Ooer, I've come over ever so wobbly.
Gloria	Just look at his mouth, it's ghastly.
Giles	I say, it's black.
Crawls	Well, you know why, don't you, sir?
Giles	I can't say I do, Inspector.
Diggins	Shall I get a cloth, madam?
Lady M.	No, I think it is too late now. I know what that is . . .
Lord M.	What's going on?
Bubbles	You mean it's . . .
Rev.	Yes, there's no doubt about it . . .
PC	That's right, sir – POISON.
Crawls	Like I said, sir – a case of MURDER.
PC	A grisly case at that.
Crawls	And very . . . FRESH. And if I'm not mistaken, the body is still . . . WARM.
Giles	Gosh, you mean he's . . . he's . . . he's sort of . . . DEAD?

Crawls	Told you so.
PC	Don't say we didn't warn you.
Rev.	Fancy that.
Gloria	How shocking.
Maud	Blimey.
Bubbles	Double Blimey!
Mrs C.	Treble Blimey! By gum and hecky thump!
Diggins	I gather we won't be needing the balloons after all, my lady?
Lord M.	What's up? Something the matter? The party seems to have gone dead all of a sudden... What is Eric doing down there? Is it another game of hunt the thimble? I say, he looks rather black around the gills.
Lady M.	He's just snuffed it, dear. He's keeled over.
Lord M.	What? Do you mean he's gone and bought it?
Maud	Ooer, I feel all funny again.
Lady M.	Eric is dead, dear. He's been done in. [*Maud faints again*]
Lord M.	Crikey, what a bother. The party was just getting going. I say, who are these chaps?

Lady M.	These are the police, dear. An Inspector Crawls – of the Yard. They've come to find the killer. Go and fetch them some tea and muffins, Diggins.
Crawls	Not while we're on duty, if you don't mind, madam. And besides, no one must leave this room.
Lord M.	I think I might have to after all that port.
Crawls	Like I said, you must all stay in here while I get to the bottom of this grim affair.
Giles	Now look here, inspector, there are ladies present.
PC	And it could be one of them did the deed, sir.
Rev.	Good heavens, you can't possibly mean one of them is the . . . MURDERER?
Crawls	Well, that depends, doesn't it?
Gloria	Good, then will someone take away the body and leave us all alone. I can't stay in this room a minute longer with those horrid eyes staring at me – wide open and bloodshot.
Crawls	The corpse is staying right there, miss.
Gloria	I'm not talking about Sir Eric – I mean *you*! You give me the creeps.

PC	We are only doing our job, madam. Nobody leaves this room.
Gloria	But I need to go out for some air.
PC	I don't think we've made ourselves clear.
Crawls	No one leaves till we've found some answers. The killer is standing here in the room. Yes, one of you right here in front of me has just poisoned Sir Eric Tweedhope, MP for Muckleby-Under-Mudflap.
Maud	er ummm
Bubbles	She's coming round. Here, give her some smelling salts.
Diggins	Shall I take her up to her room, my lady?
Crawls	No. Like I said, nobody moves, not even Maud.
Giles	Now look here, I don't like your manner, Inspector.
Crawls	I can't help that, sir. Now, everyone sit down while I ask some questions.
Lord M.	Eh? What was that?
Lady M.	He's going to ask us some questions, dear.
Lord M.	It's a bit late for a quiz, isn't it?
Lady M.	Look, Inspector, can't all this wait till the morning? We're all very tired and I can't see why any of *us* would want to kill Sir Eric.

PC	Oh, can't you, madam?
Crawls	We'll soon see about that.
PC	What about Miss Gloria? I'm sure she had a good reason.
Gloria	But . . . but . . . what do you mean by that? What I said earlier was only a sort of a . . . joke.
Crawls	And what did you say, miss?
Gloria	Only that . . . well, we just had a little row, that's all. I said if I had a New Year's wish it would be to have a dagger in my hand.
Maud	Oooer, where am I?
PC	To *kill* Sir Eric? [*Maud faints again*]
Gloria	Well yes, but . . . it was only a joke.
Crawls	Not a very funny joke, is it, miss?
Gloria	No, but well, oh dear . . . this is terrible.
PC	Just why did you hate Sir Eric so much?
Gloria	I didn't hate him that much – it's just that he was a swine. He had the theatre closed down where I was an actress and I've never been on the stage since. He had a lot of power, you see . . . and he was always so rude to me. But no one liked him. He was mean.
Crawls	So mean that you had to kill him, miss?

Lady M.	Please stop picking on Gloria, Inspector. It can't be her. She wouldn't harm a soul.
Crawls	Really, madam? She could easily have slipped poison into his port when she left the room.
Gloria	But how do you know I left the room?
Crawls	Ah, it's my job to find these things out, miss. Now let us move on. What about this young man here?
Giles	I say, steady on: Don't be batty. I mean, why on earth should I want to bump the old man off?
PC	You tell us. Have you ever felt you wanted to hit him?
Giles	Well, yes, but that was just for a tease.
Bubbles	Don't mention the bet, Giles.
Giles	Ssshh, nobody knows.
Crawls	A little matter of a gamble with Sir Eric, was it, sir?
Giles	I say, how did you guess that?
Lady M.	Is it true, Giles?

Giles	Well, er . . . yes. Sir Eric and I once had a bet after a big row. I told him he was too old and he bet me he would live longer than me. We had it all done on paper. If I die first, he'll get fifty thousand pounds in my will. And if he dies first, I'll get fifty thousand pounds.
Crawls	It looks like you've just won. Quite a good reason to kill him!
Giles	Now look here, Inspector, you don't really think I would do such a soppy thing.
PC	You had every reason to, sir. After all, it's very clear how much you hated him.
Bubbles	But we all do . . . I mean *did*. He was a beast. None of us could stand him. I hated him after what he said tonight. I could have . . .
Crawls	Yes, miss? You could have *killed* him? Is that what you were going to say?
Bubbles	Well . . . no, of course not. It's just that he was very rude to me. He was horrid to all of us.
PC	But what about your father?
Giles	I say, steady on . . . what's her old man got to do with all this?
Crawls	Sir Eric and he were good friends, I believe?
Bubbles	Yes, but that's got nothing to do with it.

PC	And does your father know of your friendship with Giles Gray, miss?
Bubbles	Well, sort of . . . he knows I like him.
Crawls	Is that so, sir?
Giles	Yes, and I don't mind telling you that her father can't stand the sight of me. He told Bubbles that if she ever saw me again, he would have nothing to do with her.
Crawls	Is your father a rich man, miss?
Bubbles	Yes, he is. Filthy rich – but he keeps it all to himself.
Crawls	So you wouldn't want to miss out on his fortune then, would you?
Bubbles	Of course not.
Giles	But don't be daft. How on earth would her father ever find out we'd been together tonight?
PC	Sir Eric? Perhaps he said that he would spill the beans?
Bubbles	How did you know?
Giles	Careful, dear, this is a trap.
Crawls	So Sir Eric was going to tell your father.

Bubbles	Well – yes, all right he was ... but ... but ... it doesn't mean to say I would *kill* Sir Eric. [*She sobs*]
Diggins	Would you like me to fetch a hanky, my lady?
Crawls	Oh no, you don't leave this room. We need to talk to you as well.
Lady M.	Oh don't be silly. Surely you don't suspect Diggins! He's been our butler for over thirty years.
PC	Ah, but what was he before that?
Diggins	I can't think what you mean, sir.
Crawls	Revenge, Diggins, can haunt a man for years.
Lady M.	I think Maud is waking up again.
Maud	Lor love us, I don't know where I am and what's going on ...
Crawls	Diggins is about to tell us how he once knew Sir Eric ... better known as ... the CORPSE. [*She faints again*]
Diggins	All right, all right. I'll tell you. Sir Eric was my boss years ago, he was a major in the army in the war. I once saved his life but one day he caught me stealing a scrap of food from the stores – to give to a poor widow whose only son was dying. He had me locked away and beaten for that. I've never forgotten it and I've been longing to pay him back ever since.

31

Crawls	So you carefully planned to poison his port.
Diggins	No, sir. I can't say I'm sorry to see him there on the floor – but it wasn't me.
Rev.	Now look here, Inspector, this really isn't fair – dragging out the past like this. You're trying to make these good people feel guilty for things that happened years ago. This is supposed to be a party. We are supposed to be having a good time – not digging up our rotten old secrets of years gone by.
PC	So *you* haven't got any secrets, is that right, Rev. Dithers?
Rev.	Of course not. I'm a bishop. I wouldn't want to kill Sir Eric.
Gloria	You wouldn't know how.
Crawls	As the actress said to the bishop! But not even if he knew the truth about you?
Rev.	Don't be absurd.
PC	Not even if he wanted to tell the newspapers?
Mrs C.	Ee by heck, he wouldn't dare. If he so much as breathed a word, I would have coshed him with my rolling pin.
Rev.	Ssshh, Gladys . . . hold your tongue.

Mrs C.	No, I won't. If that man knew you and I were going to run away together to Gretna Green, then it's just as well he's been done away with.
Crawls	Did you say, 'running away together', miss?
Giles	Crikey!
Mrs C.	Aye. We've fallen head over heels in love – Bishop Dithers and me ... and we're running away together in the morning.
Rev.	Sssh, just think of the scandal, Gladys.
Bubbles	Amazing!
PC	But Sir Eric found out, didn't he? And you, Mrs Cloggit, could have easily poisoned his supper tonight. After all, you cooked his food.
Rev.	Nonsense, she wouldn't dream of doing such a thing.
Mrs C.	No, but if I had given it a thought, I'd have done it willingly!
Maud	Cor love a duck, I'm feeling all floppy.
PC	It's just the shock, miss. After all, death can be a cruel shock. [*She faints again*]
Crawls	So you see, you *all* had a good reason to kill Sir Eric tonight.

Lady M.	Well, I certainly didn't, and I think this has all gone far enough. You have ruined our New Year's Eve party. What was just a simple little death has turned into a ghastly nightmare. My husband has fallen asleep and you've accused all our guests of a ghastly murder. Now I think you both ought to go.
PC	But what if his lordship poisoned Sir Eric?
Lord M.	Eh? What? Did somebody say something?
Crawls	Did you kill Sir Eric, Lord Muckleby?
Lord M.	Blowed if I can remember. Did I, dear?
Lady M.	Of course not. Why on earth would we want to do such a thing?
Lord M.	Yes, I can think of a good reason. Eric has wanted this place, Muckleby Manor, for years and I'm blowed if I'm going to sell it to him ... so the blighter has gone and bought the field next door and said he's going to build a great big holiday camp on our doorstep. It's enough to make you spit!
Crawls	But is it enough to make you KILL?
Lady M.	But just think, Inspector – this has been our home for years. Just imagine having a horrible holiday camp out there. We would lose everything – but he wouldn't listen to us. That's why we asked him here tonight, to try and change

	his mind. All he said was we had to move with the times. He was going to sign the papers in the morning to let them start work churning up our lovely countryside. Our own private fishing lake would be ruined.
Lord M.	I told him over my dead body!
Lady M.	He would only agree not to do it if we left him this house in our will. What an evil thing to do, don't you think so, Inspector?
Crawls	So he wouldn't listen to you?
Lord M.	No – nothing we could do could change his mind – apart from the Will.
PC	So you killed him.
Maud	I want to go home.
Lady M.	Now really, Constable, do I look like a murderer?
Maud	Help!
Crawls	You all do. In fact every one of you here could have done this. The finger could point at any one of you.
PC	The question we are all asking ourselves is 'Which one is the killer?'
Crawls	Who was it who sent him to the grave in cold blood?

PC	Every one of you has a good reason.
Crawls	And every one of you is glad he is dead.
PC	But we know the truth. It is never who you expect.
Crawls	Let that be our warning to you tonight. Things are never quite what they seem. There is much more to this than meets the eye – so be warned. Don't put all your eggs in one basket. Each one of you beware . . .
Gloria	Except Maud, poor girl. You can see she's upset. Can't we leave all this till morning?
Maud	It wasn't me, really. I didn't do it.
PC	But you were the one who brought in the tray of drinks. You were the only one who could have slipped in the deadly poison at any time.
Maud	It wasn't me, honest – cross my heart. I don't know any secrets . . . well, only one, something I heard in the . . .
Gloria	You mustn't worry, Maud. You keep it to yourself. Don't let them bully you.
Crawls	Well, if you know something, we ought to know about it. I think we need to hear it.
Maud	No . . . I couldn't – not here.
Crawls	Then we'll have to take you back to the Yard.

Lady M.	You mean she's under arrest?
PC	If you like to put it that way, madam.
Maud	Blimey, I'm not a killer. You've got to believe me. But I think I know who is because you see . . .
Crawls	Now if you'll just come along with us, miss and we'll clear up all this little matter.
PC	We'll probably be back – so don't touch anything. Now come along, miss.
Crawls	Farewell, for the time being – and remember my warning.
Maud	This ain't right . . . [*They exit, taking Maud with them*]
Lady M.	I don't believe it!
Lord M.	What's going on?
Gloria	But they've left the body!
Giles	I say! How very odd!
Bubbles	But they've made us all look pretty silly.
Rev.	I feel such a fool, Gladys. Everyone knows about us now.
Mrs C.	Aye, the cat's out the bag all right. We all know about each other's wicked ways now. What shall we do?

Lady M.	They've made us all confess.
Diggins	But what about poor Maud, my lady? She wouldn't harm a fly. She's the only one of us who is not guilty of plotting against Sir Eric.
Gloria	But she knew something – some sort of secret.
Giles	Wait a minute – what did that Inspector say his name was?
Lady M.	Inspector Crawls, wasn't it?
Lord M.	Bit of a daft name, what?
Bubbles	But didn't you notice something odd about them?
Mrs C.	Aye, right funny if you ask me. Not normal.
Rev.	They weren't like real policemen.
Diggins	Yes, sir – and that Constable. They were both rather strange.
Gloria	I suppose you're right, come to think of it.
Rev.	Perhaps they were only acting. It could have been a hoax.
Mrs C.	Aye, some kind of prank. Larking about, like.
Giles	I say, yes, of course. They just wanted to show us all up.
Bubbles	Well I don't think it's very funny.

Lady M.	But what about poor Maud?
Lord M.	Such a nice young gal.
Bubbles	Yes, I remember now. They both seemed to know who we are.
Mrs C.	How come?
Bubbles	Well that Inspector called Maud by her name before any of us had mentioned it.
Giles	I say, you clever old stick! You're right. I bet the three of them are in all this together. Some sort of plot.
Lady M.	Come to think of it, I thought something was strange as soon as I took the phone call. There was an odd whisper on the line. And surely no policemen would appear on the stroke of midnight. I don't think it was Scotland Yard at all.
Giles	Then there's one way to find out. Can I use the phone?
Lady M.	Of course – but why?
Giles	I'm going to phone Scotland Yard – to ask them if there really is such a man as Inspector Crawls. [*He picks up phone and dials*]
Lord M.	In spectacles? Are you sure he wore glasses?

Giles	Hello? Scotland Yard? Ah, good, I want to ask some questions . . .
Bubbles	But if they weren't real policemen, how did they know so much about us?
Rev.	Ah, but did they? If you remember, we just told them everything. All they did was ask the questions.
Mrs C.	And we just spilled all the beans. It makes you sick!
Diggins	Well we all fell for it good and proper. We told them everything.
Bubbles	Yes, but they still seemed to know too much for my liking.
Gloria	So what do we do now?
Lady M.	Try to find the truth. Get to the bottom of all this.
Lord M.	What was that?
Lady M.	Giles is phoning Scotland Yard, dear – to find the truth.
Giles	Yes . . . no . . . I see. Goodbye. [*He puts the phone down*]
Bubbles	Well, Giles, what did they say?

Giles	You'll all be pleased to hear that there is no such person as Inspector Crawls, nor PC Dobbs. In fact they've never heard of them. So we're safe. We've just been conned, that's all. The police don't even know about all this ... or about the murder.
Bubbles	Oh wonderful, our secrets are still hidden. Daddy will never know about tonight!
Rev.	So we can all carry on as before!
Diggins	Jolly good show!
Lady M.	But what about the body? After all, somebody must have done it. One of us must have bumped him off.
Giles	Yes, but who really cares? The fact is, he's gone! After all, we all hated him so much. Jolly good thing he's popped off, I say!
Gloria	We could say it was suicide. If we all say he killed himself, they would believe us. Whoever did it would then get away scot free!
Lord M.	Jolly good idea if you ask me. Never liked the fellow. His father was a rotter as well.
Giles	I say, yes – that plan would get us all off the hook.
Bubbles	Then what do we do about the corpse? We'll have to tell someone.

Gloria	Let's all go down to the local police station now, together. Just tell them he took his own life.
Mrs C.	Aye – make a statement, like.
Diggins	And it will all be forgotten, my lady.
Lady M.	Right, off we go then. Diggins, you can take us all in the Rolls Royce. We should all manage to squeeze in there and zoom down to the village.
Gloria	It's all right, I can go down in my sports car to give you more room. Tell you what, I'll race you down to the village!
Bubbles	But do you think we *all* ought to go?
Giles	Of course, why not? I'm all for a race – wizzo!
Bubbles	I don't really know. It's just what that Inspector said about there's more to all this than meets the eye – and not putting all your eggs in one basket. I wonder what he meant.
Giles	Nonsense. He was a fraud. Forget it.
Lord M.	Then what are we all waiting for? Let's get all this over so we can get back in time for more port.

Lady M.	Yes, come along then, everyone. We'll leave the body right where it it. I don't think it'll be going anywhere!! [*They all exit, laughing. Gloria is left alone*]
Gloria	I won't be a moment. I'll give you all a few seconds start and I'll still beat you!

Pause

I'll see you all down at the station.

Pause

Well that's it, then.

Pause

It's all right now. They've gone. We're safe.

[*The body sits up*]

Eric	Darling!
Gloria	Eric [*They hug*]
Eric	We've done it! We've got rid of them and it worked! Your acting was terrific. You were wonderful!
Gloria	Well, I'm not an actress for nothing. Mind you, you were pretty good yourself.

43

Eric	And who would have guessed we are really in love? That little row of ours must have fooled them.
Gloria	And the way you died – it was brilliant!
Eric	Did you like the black ink round the lips? Good idea, eh?
Gloria	You were great.
Eric	And now we can live here together, get married and no one will know about how we got the house and the money! All my enemies will be out the way for ever. I hope you set the fuse on the bridge.
Gloria	Of course – don't you trust me? It's all going like clockwork. [*They look at their watches, the clock strikes half-past twelve and there is a very loud SPLASH!*]
Eric	Just remember – never put all your eggs in one basket . . . or all your enemies in one Rolls Royce! Ha ha ha.
Gloria	Such perfect timing – the art of all good acting . . . and cutting off the brake cables! Such a shame about the Rolls Royce. Quite a drop over the bridge into the lake. So deep, as well.
Eric	But such a joy to think of all those idiots inside and they'll never get out!

Gloria	Too bad.
Eric	And those friends of yours, Gloria, were wonderful. What great actors they were. They did the job so well – worth every penny. They were like real policemen.
Gloria	Yes . . . but I've been meaning to tell you. I've been thinking about this.
Eric	After all, we had to get rid of Maud somehow. Let's hope they killed her quickly. She's probably lying at the bottom of a ditch right now so she'll never be able to tell a soul. She was the only one who knew the truth about us after she found us together in the garden the other day. She overheard our plans but with her out the way our secret is safe. We'll be happy forever now, Gloria dear. Ah, there's the phone. You'd better answer it. After all, a corpse can't really answer a phone, can he? [*She goes over and answers it*]
Gloria	Yes? Yes. Who? really? Mmm. Surely not. Well I never . . .
Eric	Well, even though I say it myself, it was all a wonderful plan and we've got away with it. I end up with Gloria, a lot of money from my bet with Giles, this lovely house – and I've also got rid of all my enemies in one go. Wonderful!

Gloria	Yes. No. Yes. No. I see. Goodbye. [*She puts the phone down*]
Eric	Well, what's wrong? Seen a ghost?
Gloria	I knew something was wrong. I don't understand it. That was my friend from the drama school – the one who was going to help us out by coming here tonight. The one who was going to act as the Inspector.
Eric	Yes, he was wonderful. Tell him I'll pay him double for such a splendid job.
Gloria	But darling, that's the point. He didn't do it. On the way here they crashed the car. Something made them swerve on the road . . .
Eric	Then who were those two men who were here at midnight?
Gloria	I don't know. They were nothing to do with me. I've never seen them before in my life . . . and they did seem so strange.
Eric	Then what have they done with Maud? We paid them to kill her. If they haven't got rid of her, our plan hasn't quite finished. [*The phone rings*] I'll answer it this time. [*He goes over to the phone*] Yes? Yes? Who? Really? Mmmm. Surely not. Well I never . . .

Gloria	I don't believe it. I knew that Inspector was strange. There was something odd about them both – but I couldn't really say anything. But who on earth were they?
Eric	Yes. No. Yes. No. No. I see. Goodbye. [*He puts down the phone*]
Gloria	Well – who was it, Eric?
Eric	That was Scotland Yard. Maud is there and she's told them everything. They want to speak to us urgently. An Inspector and a Constable are on their way over. They said they want to question us about a little matter of MURDER AT MUCKLEBY MANOR . . .